Better Vocals Wit[h]

CW00969180

Rockschool

A *Rockschool* Publication
www.rockschool.co.uk

Welcome To Level 2 *Male Vocals*

Welcome to the Rockschool Level 2 candidate pack for Male Vocals. This pack includes all the prepared elements needed by a candidate to take grades 4 and 5. In the book you will find exam scores for the performance pieces consisting of a vocal line and chord boxes.

The CDs have backing tracks for the technical exercises and backing tracks for each song. Examples of all the other tests contained in the exam can be found in the *Companion Guide* accompanying this series.

If you have any queries about this or any other Rockschool exam, please call us on **020 8332 6303** or email us at office@rockschool.co.uk. Visit our website http://www.rockschool.co.uk. Good luck!

Grade 4

Pieces at this grade will be of sufficient length to demonstrate developing stylistic awareness which will include appropriate tone production, awareness of rhythmic shifts, dynamics and phrasing. There will be demonstration of secure chest voice and the ability to move to head voice in a reliable manner. Pieces will require some ornamentation and improvisation to the given line to show a musical understanding. Range will be extended and there will be some use of consistent extended intervals. **One piece is to be performed from memory. Performers must use a microphone for all performance pieces.**

Grade 5

At this level the candidate will be expected to demonstrate a good understanding of stylistic matters. Pieces will be of a suitable length to reflect this and will be shown by tonal variety, stylistic rhythmic execution a broader understanding and control of dynamics and phrasing. The candidate will demonstrate both chest and head voice in a secure manner with the ability to cover wide intervals with an even tone. Pieces will have the opportunity for considerable ornamentation and improvisation. Two pieces are to be performed from memory. **Two pieces are to be performed from memory. Performers must use a microphone for all performance pieces.**

How To Use The CD

The Level 2 book contains a CD. On these you will find the backing tracks to the exercises and the songs. You should prepare the exercises and the songs using this CD to perform with in the exam.

For the scales and intervals in grades 4 and 5, the first backing track is in the key of A. You will find alternative keys for the scales at the end of the CD in all keys between B♭ and D around middle C. For the intervals, test 1, there are alternative notes from B♭ to A, and for test 2, there are alternative notes from F to E. Any of these keys can be used in the exam.

Important Information For Candidates

Candidates may use this syllabus to enter for either a *grade exam* or a *performance certificate* at grades 4 or 5. If you are entering for a *grade exam*, you will need to prepare the following elements. You will perform them in the exam in the order in which they are shown below. Full syllabus requirements can be found in the *Rockschool Vocal Syllabus Guide* which can be downloaded from www.rockschool.co.uk.

Technical exercises (15 marks). You will find four sets of exercises printed for each grade: a rhythm test, a scale test, an interval test and a Phrasing & Dynamics test.

General Musicianship Questions (5 marks). You will be asked four questions immediately after the Phrasing & Dynamics test. These questions will focus on aspects of music notation. One final question will be asked at the end of the exam. Please refer to the *Syllabus Guide* for the GMQ requirements.

Aural Tests (10 marks). There are two aural tests in each grade. Examples are printed in the *Companion Guide*. The requirements for each grade are as follows:

• **Grade 4.** You will be given a sheet with three rhythmic examples that are two bars long each. The examiner will play one of the examples on CD and you will be asked to identify the correct answer from the printed examples and clap back the rhythm. You will then be given three melodic examples in the same rhythms as above of two bars each. You will be asked to identify the test with the correct rhythm. You will then be asked to sight sing the examples and continue for two bars, ending on the tonic or the mediant. The second test will be a four bar chord sequence repeated over 8 bars. You will hear the sequence once and will be required to improvise a minor pentatonic line, paying attention to the rhythmic idea and shape on the repeat. **This test is continuous.**

• **Grade 5**. Test 1: as for Grade 4. The second test will be a four bar chord sequence repeated over 8 bars. You will hear the sequence once and will be required to improvise a minor pentatonic or blues line, paying attention to the style, rhythmic idea and shape on the repeat. **This test is continuous.**

Three performance pieces (60 marks). You are not limited solely to the songs printed in this book, or the companion Level 1 volume. You may perform **either** three songs from this book (including one or more from the supplementary list printed for each grade), **or** you may bring in **one** song not included in these lists to perform in the exam. This may be a hit from the chart or a song of your own composing. Please ensure, though, that you have the appropriate backing track. Please turn to the Guru's Guide on page 43 for the list of supplementary material.

Unaccompanied Piece (10 Marks). In addition, you will be asked to perform either a part of one of the pieces you have performed, or a different song, unaccompanied. You will be asked to sing this after you have performed the second accompanied song you have chosen. Please refer to the *Syllabus Guide* for the variation and improvisation requirements.

If you are entering a *performance certificate*, you will perform **five** songs, of which up to **two** may be from repertoire not included in this book or the companion Level 1 volume.

The Level 2 *Male Vocals* book is a companion to the Level 2 *Female Vocals* book. Candidates are welcome to perform repertoire contained in either book in the exam of equivalent difficulty.

Grade 4 *Technical Exercises*

In this section, the examiner will ask you to perform the four exercises printed below. You do not need to memorise the exercises (and you may use the book in the exam) but the examiner will be looking for the speed and confidence of your response. The examiner will also give you credit for the level of your musicality in your attention to directions, including phrasing and dynamics.

Exercise 1: Rhythm

Track 1

You will be asked to perform the exercise below as written to a backing track accompaniment in the exam. A short sound check will be given.

Exercise 2: Scales

You will be asked to perform a major, natural minor, major pentatonic and minor pentatonic scale with arpeggios in the following rhythms to a backing track accompaniment in the exam. You will be allowed to choose your own starting note between **A-D** which will be played to you before you begin. You will be asked a selection by the examiner and you will perform the exercise *legato* to a sound of your own choosing.

Major

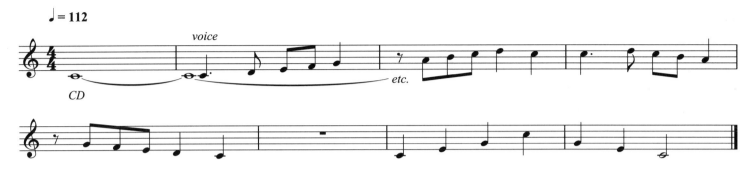

Natural Minor

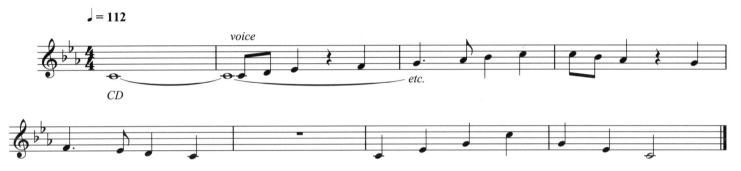

Major Pentatonic

Minor Pentatonic

Exercise 3: Intervals

This exercise has two parts. (A) You will be asked to pitch a major or minor third, perfect fourth and perfect fifth by step and back to the third above notes **I**, **IV** and **V** of the chosen key of the above scale. The examiner will play the note for four beats on a CD and you will be asked to sing as indicated.

(B) You will be asked to pitch the root to major or minor third by step and back to tonic below the perfect fifth of the tonic notes of the above test. The examiner will play the interval for four beats on a CD and you will be asked to sing as indicated.

Exercise 4: Phrasing & Dynamics

You will be asked to prepare the following exercise. The examiner will play the backing on CD and you will be asked to sing the exercise, paying attention to the written phrasing and dynamics. You may perform the exercise using any sound that you consider appropriate.

Light My Fire

Words & Music by Jim Morrison, Robbie Krieger,
Ray Manzarek & John Densmore

♩ = 108

1. You

know that it would be un-true,_____ you know that I would be a li-

(2, 3.) time to he-si-tate is through,_ there's no time to wal-low in the mire_

-ar if___ I was to say___ to___ you, girl,_____

if___ I was to say___ to___ you,

3. try___ now we could on — ly___ lose, that our

we could-n't get much high-er. } Come on ba-by light my fire._

(2, 3.) love be-comes a fun-eral py-re. }

_ Come on ba-by light_ my_ fire._ Try to set the night on fire._

Oh,_ the time _ fire._ Yeah,_ yeah,_ yeah, yeah.

She's The One

Words & Music by Karl Wallinger

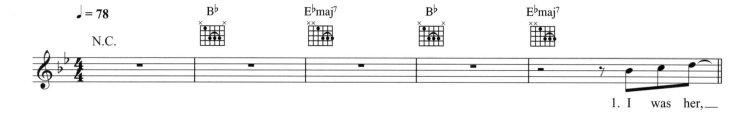

1. I was her,

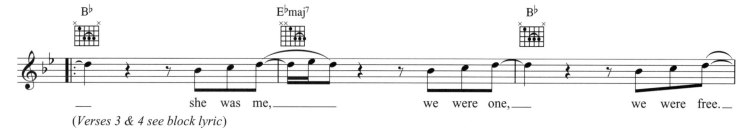

she was me,⎯⎯ we were one,⎯ we were free.

(Verses 3 & 4 see block lyric)

And if there's some-bo-dy⎯ call-ing me on,⎯ she's the one.⎯

If there's some-bo-dy⎯ call-ing me on,⎯ she's the one.⎯

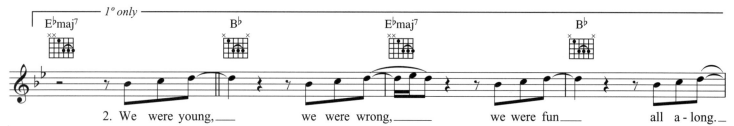

1° only

2. We were young,⎯ we were wrong,⎯ we were fun⎯ all a-long.

If there's some-bo-dy⎯ call-ing me on,⎯ she's the one.⎯

When you get to where you wan-na go,⎯ and you know the things you wan-na know,⎯ you're

Vocals Level 2 - Male

Verse 3:

Though the sea will be strong
I know we'll carry on.
'Cause if there's somebody calling me on, she's the one.
If there's somebody calling me on, she's the one.

Verse 4:

I was her, she was me
We were one, we were free.
And if there's somebody calling me on, etc .

Stereotypes

Words & Music by Damon Albarn,
Graham Coxon, Alex James & David Rowntree

Track 8

Vocals Level 2 - Male

Verse 2:

The suburbs they are sleeping but he's dressing up tonight
She likes a man in uniform, he likes to wear it tight
They're on the lover's sofa, they're on the patio
And when the fun is over, watch themselves on video.

The neighbours may be staring
But they are just past caring.

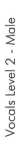

Back In The USSR

Words & Music by
John Lennon & Paul McCartney

Vocals Level 2 - Male

In The Midnight Hour

Words & Music by
Steve Cropper & Wilson Pickett

I'm gon - na wait 'til the mid - night hour, _____ that's when my

love comes tum - bl - ing ___ down. _____ I'm gon - na wait 'til the mid - night hour ___

_____ when there's no - one else ___ a - round. _____ I'm gon - na

take you girl ___ and hold ___ you and do all the things ___ I told ___

___ you in the mid - night hour. ___ Yes I am oh ___ yes I am. ___

I'm gon - na wait 'til the stars ___ come out ___ and see that twin - kle in your eyes. ___

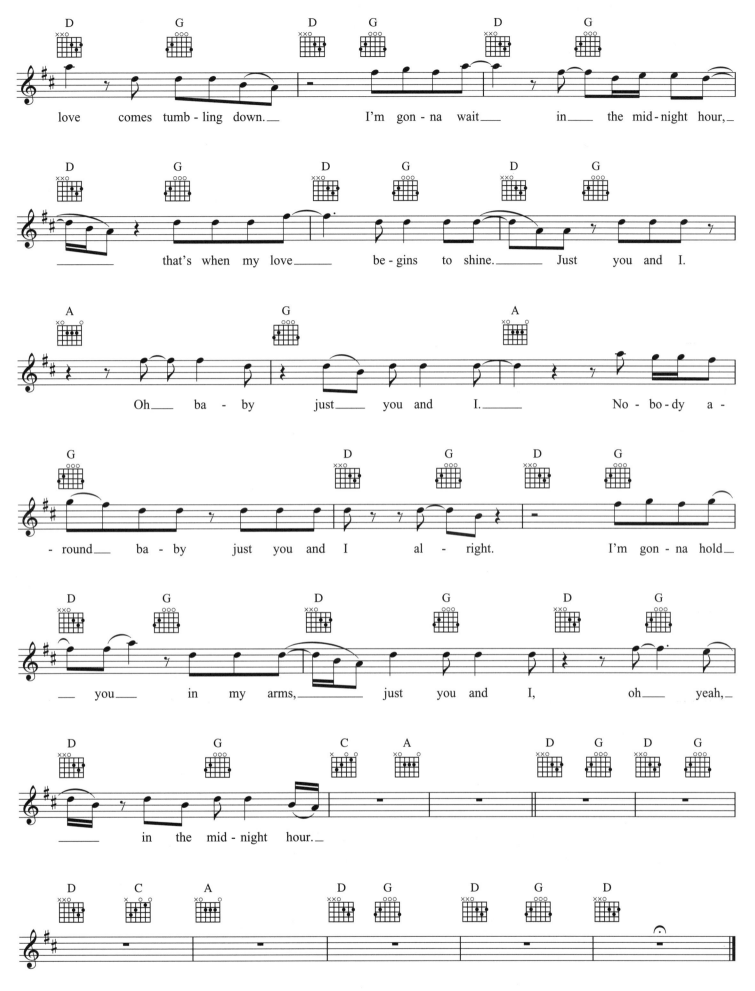

A Little Less Conversation

Words & Music by
Billy Strange & Scott Davis

Track 11

lit - tle less con - ver - sa - tion, a lit - tle more ac - tion please.

All this ag - gra - va - tion ain't__ sa - tis - fac - tion - ing me.

lit - tle more bite, a lit - tle less bark,__ a lit - tle less fight and a lit - tle__ more spark.__ Close your

mouth and op - en up your heart__ and ba - by sa - tis - fy__ me. Sa - tis - fy__

1.
__ me ba - by.

Ba - by close your eyes and lis - ten to the mu - sic dig to the sum - mer breeze.___

It's a groov - y night and I can show you how to come a - long with me and put your mind at ease.___ A

2.

Come on ba - by I'm tired of talk - in', grab your coat and let's_ start a walk - in'.

Come on, come, on. Come on, come on.

Come on, come on. Don't pro - cras - ti - nate, don't ar - tic - u - late,

girl, it's get - ting late, you just sit__ and wait a - round. A_____

Entering An Exam

Please use one, or a combination, of these forms to enter the exam(s) of your choice. Fill out the details as requested below and send the form, along with the appropriate fees, to:

Exam Entries, Rock School Ltd, 245 Sandycombe Road, Kew, Surrey, TW9 2EW

There are three examination periods per year for which you may enter. The closing dates for these are shown in the table below.

PERIOD	DURATION	CLOSING DATE
Period A	1st February to 15th March	1st December
Period B	15th May to 31st July	1st April
Period C	1st November to 15th December	1st October

You can get up-to-date information on examination prices by ringing the Rockschool help line on **020 8332 6303** Please make cheques or postal orders payable to **Rock School Ltd**.

Exam Entry Form

Full Name	
Address	
Post Code	
Telephone	
Please tick one	Grade ☐ Performance Certificates ☐
Grade	1 ☐ 2 ☐ 3 ☐ 4 ☐ 5 ☐ 6 ☐ 7 ☐ 8 ☐
Period	A ☐ B ☐ C ☐
Year	
Fee	
Dates that are absolutely impossible for you to attend:	

Teacher's Exam Entry Form

Teachers wishing to enter grade exams and performance certificates on behalf of their students should complete the form and send it, along with the appropriate fees, to

Exam Entries, Rock School Ltd, 245 Sandycombe Road, Kew, Surrey, TW9 2EW

You can get up to date information on examination prices by ringing the Rockschool help line on **020 8332 6303** Please make cheques or postal orders payable to **Rock School Ltd**.

Teacher's Name	
Address	
	Post Code
Telephone	

Name	Grade	Perf.Cert	Period	Year	Fee
				Total fees enclosed	£

Dates that are absolutely impossible for you to attend:

Vocal Exam Regulations

1. Rockschool exams are open to all persons, irrespective of age.

2. Full payment and relevant documentation must reach the offices of Rockschool on or before the chosen exam period's closing date. Rockschool cannot guarantee an exam for any applications received after this date.

3. Candidates may not transfer an exam from one exam centre to another.

4. Exam entries may not be transferred from one candidate to another.

5. Cancellation of an exam will result in loss of the exam fee unless as a result of illness or injury. Such cases must be substantiated by a medical certificate. In this event, the exam will be re-scheduled on receipt of half of the original exam fee.

6. On application, candidates may state times within an exam period when they are unavailable. However, Rockschool cannot guarantee to avoid all such dates.

7. Rockschool reserves the right to defer exams until the next available exam period. After one deferral, an exam is guaranteed at an exam centre chosen by Rockschool. This may not be your local centre.

8. Candidates must use only the official Rockschool sheet music for their respective exam. Photocopying of any material contained within the official published pack is prohibited. You may not use a Rockschool pack already used by someone else in another exam. This will result in disqualification.

9. No refunds are given.

10. No teacher, or other person, must be present during the preparation of a candidate's Quick Study Piece. Any assistance given to a candidate will result in disqualification from the examination.

11. Only the examiner and candidate are allowed to be present in the examination room with the exception of external moderators or trainee examiners.

12. Candidates must bring in two copies of music for the 'free choice piece'. Players must use an original copy of the tune to be performed, and must provide a second copy for the examiner, which may be a photocopy. If there is no music available, a zero mark will be given for the piece. Any queries in writing should be addressed to the General Manager at least two weeks prior to the exam date.

13. Any special needs candidates must notify the Rockschool office prior to the exam.

14. The examiner's decision is final. Normally, an examiner will hear every component in full, but on occasion an examiner may conclude an examination when a decision has been reached.

15. Rockschool operates a quality assured appeals process, moderated by Trinity College London. All appeals must be made in writing no later than 14 days after the exam date. There are two criteria for formal appeals, these are:
    - Appeals in respect of errors in procedure.
    - Appeals in respect of errors in matching comments to marks awarded.

16. Candidates may use microphones for the lower grades (grades 1-5) but must inform the office of their intention to do so.

Grade 5 *Technical Exercises*

In this section, the examiner will ask you to perform the four exercises printed below. You do not need to memorise the exercises (and you may use the book in the exam) but the examiner will be looking for the speed and confidence of your response. The examiner will also give you credit for the level of your musicality in your attention to directions, including phrasing and dynamics.

Exercise 1: Rhythm

Track 12

You will be asked to perform the exercise below as written to a backing track accompaniment in the exam. A short sound check will be given.

Exercise 2: Scales

You will be asked to perform a major and natural minor with arpeggios and a minor pentatonic and blues scale in the following rhythms to a backing track accompaniment in the exam. You will be allowed to choose your own starting note between **A-D** which will be played to you before you begin. You will be asked a selection by the examiner and you will perform the exercise *legato* or *staccato* to a sound of your own choosing.

Major Scale and Arpeggio
Track 13

to be prepared *legato* and *staccato*

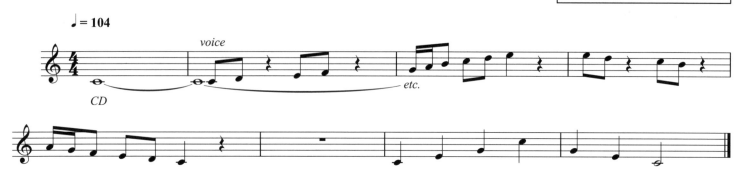

Natural Minor Scale and Arpeggio
Track 14

Minor Pentatonic Scale
Track 15

Blues Scale
Track 15

Exercise 3: Intervals

You should prepare all three parts of a chordal sequence using chords **I**, **IV** and **V**. The examiner will select the part to be given against the other two parts played on a backing track.

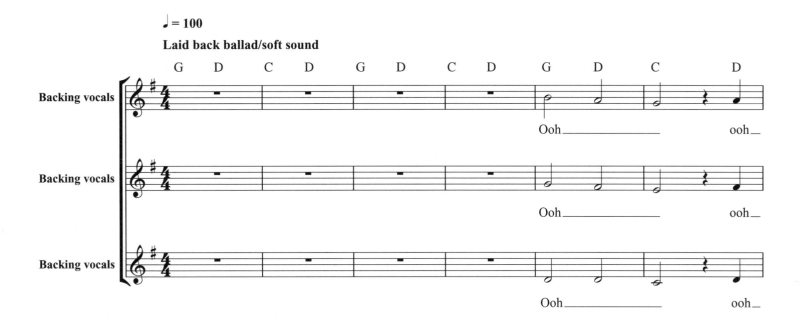

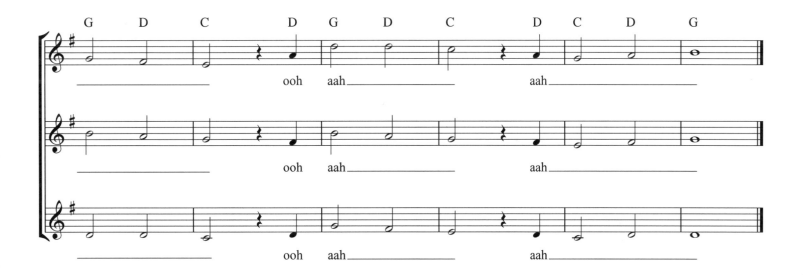

Exercise 4: Phrasing & Dynamics

You will be asked to prepare the following exercise. The examiner will play the backing on CD and you will be asked to sing the exercise, paying attention to the written phrasing and dynamics. You may perform the exercise using any sound that you consider appropriate.

Let Me Entertain You

Words & Music by
Robbie Williams & Guy Chambers

Track 20

1. Hell is gone and hea-ven's here,____ there's no-thing left__ for you to fear,____
2. Life's too short for you to die____ so grab your-self__ an a-li-bi____

shake your arse come ov-er here, now scream. I'm a burn-ing ef-fi-gy__ of
hea-ven knows your mo-ther lied, mon cher. Se-pa-rate your right from wrongs,__

ev-'ry-thing I used to be you're my rock of em-pa-thy my dear. So come on
come and sing a dif-ferent song the ket-tle's on so don't_ be long mon cher. So come on

let me_____ en-ter-tain____ you,

let me_____ en-ter-tain____ you.

Look me up in the yel-low pa-ges I will be your rock of a-ges, you

Vocals Level 2 - Male

Let me_____ en - ter - tain_____ you.

Come on, come on, come on,_____ come on,_____ come on, come on, come on,_____ come on,_____

come on, come on, come on,_____ come on,_____

Let me en - ter - tain_____ you let me en - ter - tain_____ you.

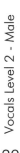

Stand By Me

Words & Music by Ben E. King,
Jerry Leiber & Mike Stoller

Track 21

♩ = 60

N.C.

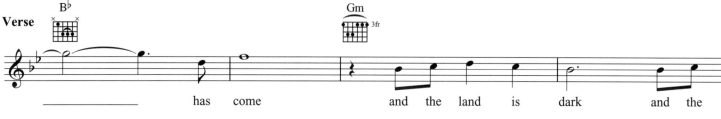

1. When the night

Verse

B♭   Gm

has come   and the land is dark   and the

E♭   F⁷   B♭

moon   is the on-ly   light we'll see.   No, I

Gm

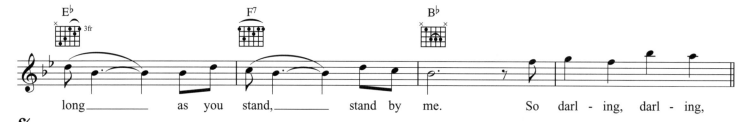

won't be a-fraid, no   I won't be a-fraid,   just as

E♭   F⁷   B♭

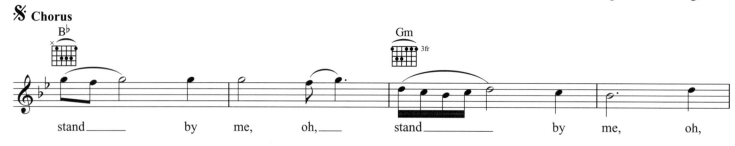

long   as you stand,   stand by me.   So darl-ing, darl-ing,

𝄋 Chorus

B♭   Gm

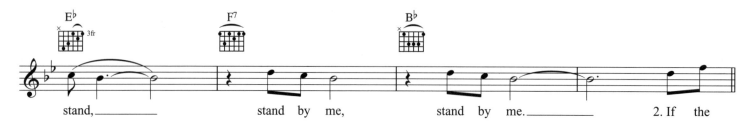

stand   by me,   oh,   stand   by me,   oh,

E♭   F⁷   B♭

stand,   stand by me,   stand by me.   2. If the

Livin' La Vida Loca

Words & Music by
Desmond Child & Robi Rosa

Track 22

1. She's in-to su-per-sti - tion, black cats and voo-doo dolls.____

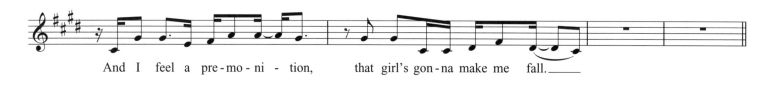

And I feel a pre-mo-ni - tion, that girl's gon-na make me fall.____

2. She's in-to new sen-sa-tions, new kicks in the can-dle-light.____ She's got a new ad-dic - tion,
(Verse 3 see block lyric)

s'full ev-'ry day and night.____ She'll make you take__ your clothes__ off and__ go dan-

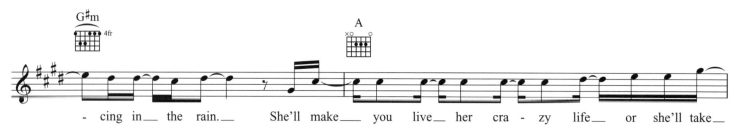

- cing in__ the rain. She'll make__ you live__ her cra-zy life__ or she'll take__

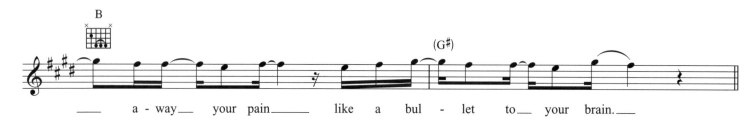

____ a-way__ your pain____ like a bul - let to__ your brain.____

Vocals Level 2 · Male

Up - side, in - side out, she's liv - in' la vi - da lo - ca. She'll

push and pull you down, liv - in' la vi - da lo - ca. Her

lips are de - vil red and her skin's the co - lour of moc - ca. Her

She will wear you out, liv - in' la vi - da lo - ca.

Liv - in' la vi - da lo - ca, she's liv - in' la vi - da lo - ca.

1.

2.

She'll make you take your clothes off and go dan -

- cing in the rain. She'll make you live her cra - zy life or she'll take

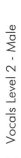

Verse 3:

Woke up in New York City
In a funky cheap hotel
She took my heart and she took my money
She must have slipped me a sleepin' pill.
She never drinks the water
Makes you order French champagne
And once you've had a taste of her
You'll never be the same
Yeah, she'll make you go insane.

Upside, inside out *etc.*

A Thousand Trees

Words by Kelly Jones
Music by Kelly Jones, Richard Jones & Stuart Cable

Track 23

Vocals Level 2 - Male

Cum On Feel The Noize

Words & Music by
Jim Lea & Noddy Holder

Vocals Level 2 - Male

(Everything I Do) I Do It For You

Words by Bryan Adams & Robert John Lange
Music by Michael Kamen

Intro

Verse

1. Look in-to my eyes, you will see what you mean to me. Search your
2. Look in-to your heart, you will find there's no-thing left to hide. So take me as I

heart, search your soul, and when you find me there, you'll
am, take my life, I would give it all I would

search no more. Don't tell me it's not worth try-in' for, you can't
sac-ri-fice. Don't tell me it's not worth fight-in' for, I can't

tell me it's not worth dy-in' for. You know it's true,
help it, there's no-thing I want more.

1.

ev-ry-thing I do, I do it for you.

2. you. Oh yeah. There's no love like your love and no

Vocals Level 2 - Male

The Guru's Guide To Level 2 *Male Vocals*

Supplementary Material

Rockschool recommends the following songs in addition to the repertoire printed in this book. The list below shows the songs arranged by grade along with the publications in which they may be found.

Grade 4

Me And Julio Down By The Schoolyard	*Play Acoustic Guitar With Paul Simon*	PS11469
Faith	*You're The Voice: George Michael*	IMP9007A
Suspicious Minds	*Sing With Elvis*	AM975172
Mack The Knife	*Sing With Pop Idols*	AM974116
Ziggy Stardust	*Play Guitar With David Bowie*	AM955988
Jumping Jack Flash	*Play Guitar With The Rolling Stones*	AM90247
She's Electric	*Play Guitar With Oasis*	AM935330
Dear Prudence	*Play Guitar With The Beatles Vol. 2*	NO90667
No Woman No Cry	*Play With Bob Marley*	EMF100617
What Becomes Of The Broken Hearted	*Sing & Party With Tear-jerkers*	IMP9803A
Evergreen	*Sing With Pop Idols*	AM974116

Grade 5

Father Figure	*You're The Voice: George Michael*	IMP9007A
Goodbye Yellow Brick Road	*Play Piano With Elton John*	AM955526
Blaze of Glory	*Play Guitar With Bon Jovi - Early Years*	AM971256
If You Don't Know Me By Now	*Sing & Party With Tear-jerkers*	IMP9803A
Eternity	*Essential Audition Songs: Pop Ballads*	IMP9776A
If You Come Back	*Sing 16 Hits*	AM976800
The Riverboat Song	*Play Guitar With... The Platinum Book*	AM951918
Achilles Heel	*Play Piano With Coldplay, Toploader Plus...*	AM970849

Warm Up

It is important that you prepare for the exam by warming up your voice properly. You should ensure that you arrive at the exam centre within plenty of time to do this. We have arranged the elements of the grade exam such that the performances come at the end. The backing tracks and/or accompaniment are always variable in volume and you should always tell the examiner if you feel that you are straining to be heard.

Free Choice Pieces

In grade exams you are allowed to perform one song not specified in this book or the companion Level 2 *Female Vocals* book. This maybe a hit from the chart or a song composed by yourself. In performance certificate exams you are allowed to perform up to two songs not specified in this book.

If you wish to find out whether a free choice piece song is appropriate for the grade, you may either contact Rockschool and submit the song for adjudication, or look on our website www.rockschool.co.uk and consult the free choice piece criteria.

Marking Schemes

The table below shows the marking schemes for grad exams and performance certificates. All Rockschool exams are marked out of 100 and the pass mark for a grade exam is 65% and for a performance certificate is 70%.

Grade Exam

Element	Pass	Merit	Distinction
Technical Exercises	11 out of 15	12 out of 15	13 out of 15
General Musicianship Questions	3 out of 5	4 out of 5	5 out of 5
Aural Tests	6 out of 10	7 out of 10	8 out of 10
Piece 1	13 out of 20	15 out of 20	17 out of 20
Piece 2	13 out of 20	15 out of 20	17 out of 20
Piece 3	13 out of 20	15 out of 20	17 out of 20
Unaccompanied Piece	6 out of 10	7 out of 10	7 out of 10

Performance Certificate

Element	Pass	Merit	Distinction
Piece 1	14 out of 20	16 out of 20	18 out of 20
Piece 2	14 out of 20	16 out of 20	18 out of 20
Piece 3	14 out of 20	16 out of 20	18 out of 20
Piece 4	14 out of 20	16 out of 20	18 out of 20
Piece 5	14 out of 20	16 out of 20	18 out of 20

Examination Criteria

Rockschool examiners assess all examinations according to strict guidelines. Copies of these for vocals can be found on the website www.rockschool.co.uk or direct from our offices. Please ring **020 8332 6303** for further details.

Exam Regulations

Entering a Rockschool exam is easy. Please read through the instructions on the back of the entry form accompanying this book carefully, before filling it in. Information on current fees can be obtained by ringing Rockschool on **020 8332 6303** or by logging on to the website www.rockschool.co.uk.